THE NUTCRACKER SUITE

by Peter Ilich Tchaikowsky
arranged by
JAMES BASTIEN

Contents

ISBN 0-8497-5068-7

The Composer

Peter Ilich Tchaikowsky (1840-1893) was born in Votkinsk, a small town in Russia. His father, an engineer, was a mining inspector in Votkinsk.

Peter was one of five children. He was described by the Swiss governess who taught the children as a sensitive studious child, but morbidly highstrung. When he was seven his mother began to teach him the piano, but she was a poor pianist and was not able to provide him with a very good foundation. Peter was also given lessons for a short time by a local teacher.

When he was ten he was placed in a boarding school in St. Petersburg (now called Leningrad), the same city his family now lived in. The pain of parting from his family and friends, especially with his mother, was severe for the young Peter. Four years later his mother died of cholera, and he was grief stricken.

Tchaikowsky studied law at the boarding school; during this time he also continued his music lessons. Upon graduation at nineteen he became a clerk at the Ministry of Justice. He persuaded his father to allow him to take courses at the St. Petersburg Conservatory. He then began to study music seriously.

He had excellent instruction with Anton Rubinstein, a pianist and composer. Tchaikowsky showed so much ability that he was appointed professor of composition at the Moscow Conservatory.

When he was thirty-seven he married Antonia Milyukova. The marriage was a very unhappy one and they lived together for only a short time. He suffered a nervous breakdown and his brother, Modest, nursed him back to health.

Fortunately, Tchaikowsky was financially supported for fourteen years by a wealthy widow, Madame von Meck. Although he never met the woman, they exchanged letters frequently. Tchaikowsky suffered another breakdown when Madame von Meck abruptly withdrew her support.

In 1891 he was invited to spend a month in the United States where he conducted six concerts of his works. When he returned to Russia he completed his sixth symphony, the **Pathetique**, in the depths of depression. Nine days after conducting the premiere Tchaikowsky died from drinking contaminated water during a cholera epidemic.

This moody composer left numerous great masterpieces including six symphonies, the **1812 Overture**, many songs, the famous **Piano Concerto Number 1**, a violin concerto, eleven operas, and the ballets **Swan Lake, The Sleeping Beauty,** and **The Nutcracker Suite.**

The Story of the Nutcracker Suite

The Silberhaus family is beginning their annual Christmas Eve party. A large brightly decorated Christmas tree stands in the middle of the room, and a fire crackles merrily in the fireplace. The two children, Clara and Fritz, run about excitedly as the guests arrive.

A new arrival enters. It is the elderly Herr Drosselmeyer with several gifts tucked under his arm. He has a beautiful doll for Clara and some handsome toy soldiers for Fritz. A most unusual gift is presented last. It is an enormous nutcracker shaped like a person—complete with head, arms, and legs. Herr Drosselmeyer shows the children how to crack a nut by placing it in the nutcracker's mouth and squeezing its jaws together. The children take turns cracking nuts, then they begin to fight over who should hold the nutcracker the longest. As Clara tries to pull it out of Fritz's hands, the nutcracker falls to the floor and breaks. The children, upset and tired, are sent off to bed.

Later, at midnight, Clara creeps down the stairs to the living room to look again at the nutcracker. She is amazed that it now looks like Herr Drosselmeyer! As she looks around she sees mice scampering about in the corners of the room. Terrified, she climbs up onto a chair and the mice vanish. Clara might have fallen asleep . . . is she dreaming? The Christmas tree begins to grow in size and the toys spring to life.

At this point a great army of mice, led by the Mouse King, appears. The nutcracker jumps up and a battle rages. Just when it seems that the nutcracker might be beaten, Clara throws her slipper towards the Mouse King who dies instantly. The army of mice quickly disappears into the woodwork.

Before Clara's eyes the nutcracker begins to grow larger and larger and is transformed into a handsome prince. As a reward for saving his life he offers an invitation to Clara to visit his kingdom, which she eagerly accepts.

Snow is falling and the ground is completely white as Clara and the prince walk in an enchanted forest. The King and Queen of Snow come forward to greet the visitors. To her amazement Clara discovers that the forest is made entirely of sweets. All the whiteness is sugar and all the ice is rock candy!

A boat appears and takes Clara and the Prince off to the royal palace of the Kingdom of Sweets. They are welcomed at the court by the Sugar-Plum Fairy. She leads them into the great hall of the palace where they sit on the Royal Throne to be entertained. A number of dances are presented for them: an Arab dance, a Chinese dance, a Russian dance, and many others.

The entire court joins in the final waltz. Clara appears to be a real princess as she sits on the miniature throne. She dreams that she lives happily ever after with the Prince in this enchanted kingdom.

Tchaikowsky was commissioned to write **The Nutcracker** using the book by M.I. Petipa based on Alexandre Dumas's version of a story by E.T.A. Hoffman. The first performance was given in 1892. The United States premiere did not take place until 1940 when the Ballet Russe de Monte Carlo performed it in New York City.

First an overture, then up with the curtain and on with the show!*

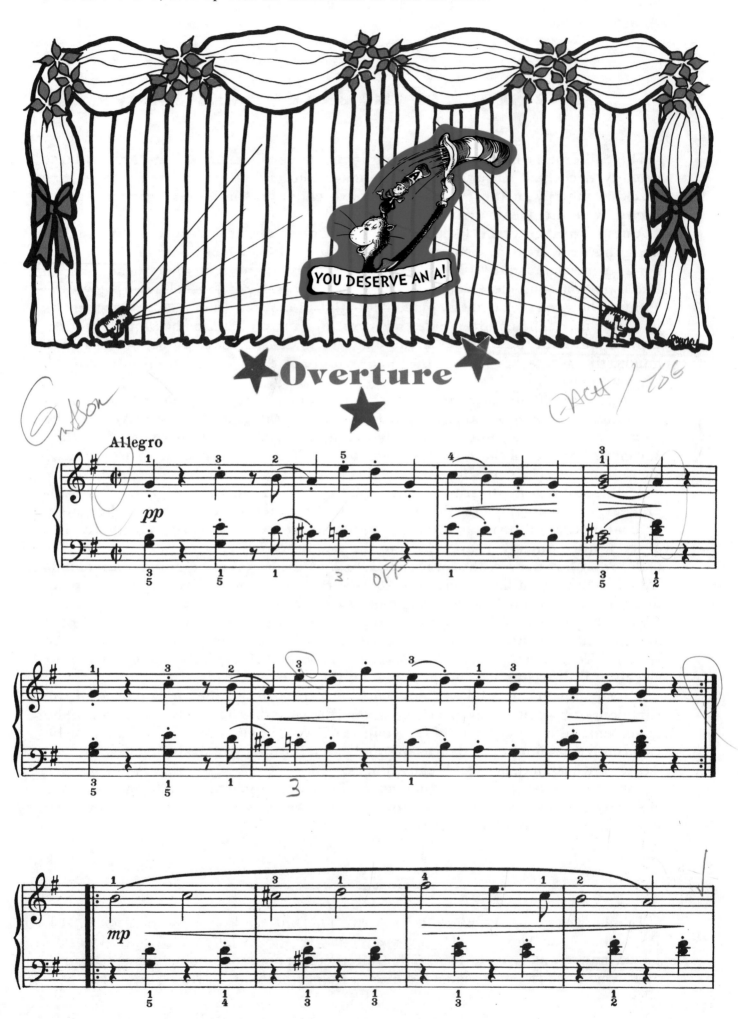

*These brief descriptions may be used to narrate a Christmas recital.

6

A march to celebrate Christmas eve. Then on with the presents!

March

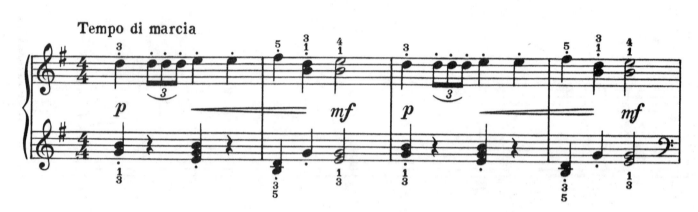

Tempo di marcia

Clara and the Prince enter into the enchanted kingdom of the Sweets and ascend the Royal Throne.

Dance of the Sugar-Plum Fairy

10

Accompanied by cymbals crashing, brightly dressed Cossacks kick their boots high in a wild fantastic dance to the amazement of all watching!

Russian Dance

"Trepak"

12

From far-off Persia comes the mysterious veiled Arabian dancer who casts
a hypnotic spell on the watchers.

Arab Dance

Well Done!

I'm Proud of You

A bearded Chinaman leaps to and fro with his partner making Clara laugh with his strange gestures.

Chinese Dance

Toy flutes come to life and perform a delicate dance swaying in the moonlight.

Dance of the Reed Pipes

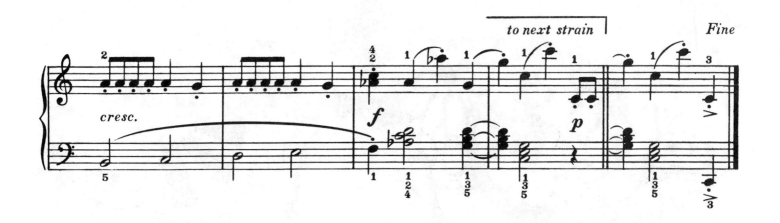

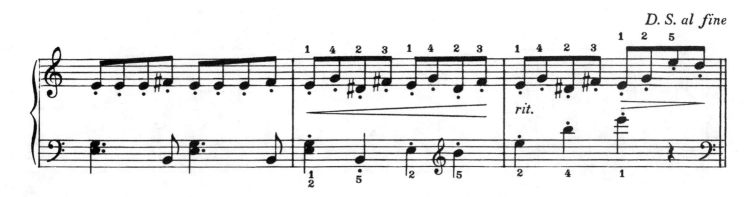

Hail Clara, a tribute to her for saving the Prince's life. In her honor, a lovely waltz.

Waltz of the Flowers

Tempo di valse

20

WP67